THE BOOK OF
Isaiah 44~66

ONE CHAPTER A DAY

GoodMorningGirls.org

The Book of Isaiah 44-66

© 2021 Women Living Well Ministries, LLC

Welcome to Good Morning Girls! We are so glad you are joining us.

God created us to walk with Him, to know Him, and to be loved by Him. He is our living well, and when we drink from the water He continually provides, His living water will change the entire course of our lives.

Jesus said: "Whoever drinks of the water that I will give him will never be thirsty again. The water that I will give him will become in him a spring of water welling up to eternal life." ~ John 4:14 (ESV)

So let's begin.

The method we use here at GMG is called the **SOAK** method.

- **S**—The S stands for *Scripture*—Read the chapter for the day. Then choose 1-2 verses and write them out word for word. (There is no right or wrong choice— just let the Holy Spirit guide you.)

- **O**—The O stands for *Observation*—Look at the verse or verses you wrote out. Write 1 or 2 observations. What stands out to you? What do you learn about the character of God from these verses? Is there a promise, command or teaching?

- **A**—The A stands for *Application*—Personalize the verses. What is God saying to you? How can you apply them to your life? Are there any changes you need to make or an action to take?

- **K**—The K stands for *Kneeling in Prayer*—Pause, kneel and pray. Confess any sin God has revealed to you today. Praise God for His word. Pray the passage over your own life or someone you love. Ask God to help you live out your applications.

SOAK God's word into your heart and squeeze every bit of nourishment you can out of each day's scripture reading. Soon you will find your life transformed by the renewing of your mind!

Walk with the King!

Courtney

WomenLivingWell.org, GoodMorningGirls.org

Join the GMG Community

*Share your daily SOAK on **Facebook.com/GoodMorningGirlsWLW***

Instagram: WomenLivingWell #GoodMorningGirls

———————————————— ❧ ————————————————

GMG Bible Coloring Chart

COLORS	KEYWORDS
PURPLE	God, Jesus, Holy Spirit, Saviour, Messiah
PINK	women of the Bible, family, marriage, parenting, friendship, relationships
RED	love, kindness, mercy, compassion, peace, grace
GREEN	faith, obedience, growth, fruit, salvation, fellowship, repentance
YELLOW	worship, prayer, praise, doctrine, angels, miracles,power of God, blessings
BLUE	wisdom, teaching, instruction, commands
ORANGE	prophecy, history, times, places, kings, genealogies, people, numbers, covenants, vows, visions, oaths, future
BROWN/GRAY	Satan, sin, death, hell, evil, idols, false teachers, hypocrisy, temptation

Introduction to the Book of Isaiah

The name Isaiah means *salvation is of the Lord*. Isaiah brought to Israel and Judah, a message of judgement for their rebellion but also a message of hope for salvation, through the coming Messiah.

For the first part of Isaiah, Isaiah focuses on God's judgement of Israel. Isaiah's message is one of condemnation for their faithless rebellion against God. God's people had turned their back on God and had become like the other nations around them. God would use the Assyrians and Babylonians to bring judgement upon them. Isaiah called on God's people to turn back and seek the Lord and he assures them that after judgement, a godly remnant would remain.

For the second part of Isaiah, Isaiah announces that Israel's punishment and exile is over, and salvation has come. We see that God is faithful to his covenant promises. No other prophet is quoted in the New Testament as much as Isaiah. Isaiah foretold the coming King of Israel, who would rule in justice and peace and would bear their sins.

The book of Isaiah offers the most complete prophetic picture of Jesus Christ in the entire Old Testament. Some of the prophecies fulfilled in Christ from the book of Isaiah are: he would be born of a virgin (Isaiah 7:14), he would be spit on and struck (Isaiah 50:6), he would be disfigured by suffering (Isaiah 52:14; 53:2), he would be rejected (Isaiah 53:1-3), he would bear our sins (Isaiah 53:4-5, 12), he would voluntarily die like a lamb to the slaughter (Isaiah 53:7), he would heal the blind, lame, deaf, diseased, broken hearted and raise from the dead (Isaiah 26:19, Isaiah 29:18-19, Isaiah 61:1-2) he would be buried in a rich man's tomb (Isaiah 53:9) and he would return to claim his own (Isaiah 60:2-3). Because of all of these prophecies fulfilled in Christ, this book is a book of hope and salvation from the Lord.

The Purpose: God used Isaiah to proclaim judgement to his people, so they would repent and turn back to him. He also used Isaiah's message of coming hope and salvation, to be a comfort to them.

The Author: Isaiah was a well-educated prophet, who was married, with two children. Tradition holds that Isaiah was martyred by being sawn in two. Isaiah ministered during the reign of Uzziah, Jotham, Ahaz and Hezekiah. Isaiah was a contemporary to the prophets Hosea and Micah. More about Israel's history during this time period can be found in 2 Kings 15-21 and 2 Chronicles 26-33.

Time Period: 740-680 B.C.

Key Verse: Isaiah 55:11

> *So shall my word be that goes from my mouth;*
> *it shall not return to me empty,*
> *but it shall accomplish that which I purpose,*
> *and shall succeed in the thing for which I sent it.*

The Outline:

Message of Judgement (1-35)

- The coming judgement of Israel and Judah (1-5)
- Isaiah's calling (6-7)
- Judgement and hope (8-12)
- Judgement of the other nations (13-24)
- Promised restoration (25-27)
- Judgement and salvation (28-35)

Isaiah and Hezekiah (36-39)

Messages of Comfort and Salvation (40-66)

- The Lord's plan of restoration for Israel (40-45)
- The fall of Babylon (46-48)
- Salvation through the servant (49-56)
- Call to repentance (57-59)
- Glorious salvation (60-65)
- God's righteous and final judgement (66)

Despite God giving Israel multiple chances to repent and turn from their ways, they continued in their sin and rebellion. As a result, God's judgement was upon them. But even through all of the dark times, God was still at work among His people. Eventually, salvation would come through the Messiah. God keeps his covenant promises to his people. We serve a faithful God, who loves us.

So, let's get started studying His word! Some of the chapters are quite long, so be sure to leave at least 20 minutes for your reading each day. I can't wait to see how God reveals himself personally to each of us, as we read the book of Isaiah together, chapter by chapter.

Keep walking with the King!

Courtney

I am the first and I am the last;

besides me there is no god.

Isaiah 44:6

Reflection Question:

Isaiah 43 ends with God warning his people of coming judgement and Isaiah 44 opens with God inviting his people to turn back to him. In their foolishness, they had turned to handmade idols. And the Lord, the King of Israel said: *"I am the first and I am the last; besides me there is no god."* An idol has a beginning because someone has to make it and it has an ending—it may break or get old, but God is self-existing with no beginning and no end. There is no god like our God!

In Revelation 1:8, Jesus says he is the Alpha and Omega, the beginning and the end. He is eternal, all powerful and worthy of all of our worship. Our God is a solid rock and foundation to build our life upon. But sometimes we can be tempted to take our focus and trust off of God and put it onto other things. An idol can be anything or anyone that takes the place of God in our lives. It may be a sinful thing, but it could actually be a good thing as well. Is there anything in your life that is pulling you away from God? Has it become an idol? Confess it now to the Lord and renew your steadfast love to God.

S—The S stands for *Scripture*

O—The O stands for *Observation*

A—The A stands for *Application*

K—The K stands for *Kneeling in Prayer*

Turn to me and be saved,

all the ends of the earth!

For I am God, and there is no other.

Isaiah 45:22

Reflection Question:

Isaiah prophesied 200 years before Cyrus was even born that he would be the deliverer of Israel. God sovereignly planned to raise him up and use him for his purposes and his plans. Over and over this passage focuses on how God is the creator, and he is in control of all things. There is no other God in all the earth. He alone saves and all we must do to be saved is to simply turn to him and repent and believe.

God created the heavens and the earth, and he also created salvation and righteousness. He made both the physical and spiritual world—the seen and unseen. He is the Lord and there is no other God but him. How does your faith grow when you consider how great, mighty and sovereign your God is? In what area of your life do you need to trust him more?

S—The S stands for *Scripture*

O—The O stands for *Observation*

A—The A stands for *Application*

K—The K stands for *Kneeling in Prayer*

Even to your old age I am he,

and to gray hairs I will carry you.

I have made, and I will bear;

I will carry and will save.

Isaiah 46:4

Reflection Question:

God named and called out the false gods that had failed to save Israel. The Babylonian gods had been humiliated and taken into captivity. While these idols had to be carried by the people as they rode on their donkeys into captivity, the God of Israel made it clear that he both carries and delivers his people.

God will never leave you. He made you. He will carry you and save you. From your birth into old age, he is completely faithful. How have you experienced God carrying you in in the past? How does it encourage you to be reminded that in the future, when you are gray haired and old in age, he will continue to carry you?

Isaiah 46

S—The S stands for ***Scripture***

O—The O stands for ***Observation***

A—The A stands for ***Application***

K—The K stands for ***Kneeling in Prayer***

Our Redeemer—

the Lord of hosts is his name—

is the Holy One of Israel.

Isaiah 47:4

Reflection Question:

Babylon was proud of their defeat of Judah and Jerusalem, but Babylon did not know that God was allowing them to win because he was using them to judge his people. They had grown prideful, so God turned and humbled Babylon. As Isaiah watches God at work saving his people and bringing Babylon low, he praises God as the Lord of Hosts, the Holy One of Israel.

Isaiah calls God their redeemer. He paid the price for his people. Isaiah calls God the Lord of Hosts. He is powerful in battle. And Isaiah calls God the Holy One of Israel. He is pure and righteous and all he does is good. He is worthy of all praise. In what area of your life has God blessed you with a talent, success or something good? Are you ever tempted to be prideful about this and in what ways? How does remembering that it is God who deserves the praise for the gifts and talents you have been given, humble you?

S—The S stands for *Scripture*

O—The O stands for *Observation*

A—The A stands for *Application*

K—The K stands for *Kneeling in Prayer*

My glory

I will not give to another.

Isaiah 48:11

Reflection Question:

God used affliction to refine Israel for his name sake. A refiner uses very high temperatures to heat metal, so he can purify the metal and skim the debris off of the top. In the same way, the affliction God brought on Israel purified them and helped to remove their sin.

God knows it is for our good that we would be close to him and obey him. He created us to know him, love him and praise him. So, when we rebel against him, not only does it displease God, but God knows it is not what is best for us. His love for us, motivates him to refine us. When in your life has God put you through a refining fire? Now that it's over, how can you see that God was lovingly doing what was best for you?

S—The S stands for *Scripture*

O—The O stands for *Observation*

A—The A stands for *Application*

K—The K stands for *Kneeling in Prayer*

Can a woman forget her nursing child,

that she should have no compassion on the son of her womb?

Even these may forget,

yet I will not forget you.

Behold, I have engraved you on the palms of my hands.

Isaiah 49:15 & 16

Reflection Question:

God's love and care for his people is greater than that of a nursing mother. He will not forget them. He says his people are engraved on the palm of his hands. This engraving is referring to a mark that cannot be erased. This was fulfilled through the scars on Jesus' hands. After Jesus died on the cross, he showed his nail scarred hands to Thomas. (John 20:27). There is no greater picture of God's love than this!

Do you ever feel forgotten by God? Isaiah felt this way in Isaiah 40:27, when he said he felt hidden from the Lord. David felt this way many times in the book of Psalms. Even Jesus cried out on the cross, *"My God, my God, why have you forsaken me?"* (Matthew 27:46). Friends, God never forgets you! He is always with you and is completely faithful. In what area of your life are you tempted to doubt God? Write a prayer below asking God to help you trust him more.

S—The S stands for *Scripture*

O—The O stands for *Observation*

A—The A stands for *Application*

K—The K stands for *Kneeling in Prayer*

But the Lord God helps me;

therefore I have not been disgraced;

therefore I have set my face like a flint,

and I know that I shall not be put to shame.

Isaiah 50:7

Reflection Question:

In Isaiah 50:6, Isaiah prophesied of the suffering that Jesus would endure as he was beaten and spit on. Jesus gave his back to those who struck him. With his face set like flint, Jesus endured the humiliation of the cross and gave himself voluntarily for you and me. Is there any greater love?

Despite the extreme suffering Jesus was about to face, he did not waver. He was determined to fulfill God's plan and mission for him. Friends, the race God has marked out for us takes perseverance. On hard days, we must press on with our face set like flint, to complete our calling. In what areas have you grown tired and weary? How does remembering what Christ has suffered for you, give you the strength to press on no matter what the cost.

S—The S stands for *Scripture*

O—The O stands for *Observation*

A—The A stands for *Application*

K—The K stands for *Kneeling in Prayer*

Listen to me,

you who pursue righteousness,

you who seek the Lord:

look to the rock from which you were hewn.

Isaiah 51:1

Reflection Question:

Three times in this chapter the Lord says to his people, "Listen to me." They were discouraged and he wanted them to pay attention, so he could comfort them. He wanted them to be reminded of how he had worked in the past through just one man alone, Abraham. God kept his promises to him and multiplied him and he would keep his promises to them too.

The enemy likes to use discouragement of God's people to cause us to not trust in him. But we are encouraged when we remember the amazing work he has done in our own life and the lives of others. God is the same yesterday, today and forever and he is at work in our lives even when we don't see it. He is a promise keeping God. Are you discouraged right now? Think back to a time when you saw God at work in your own life or in the life of a friend and write about it below. Take comfort in knowing that the same God, who was at work in the past, is at work in your life now. Do not let the enemy discourage you. God sees you and he loves you.

Isaiah 51

S—The S stands for *Scripture*

O—The O stands for *Observation*

A—The A stands for *Application*

K—The K stands for *Kneeling in Prayer*

For the Lord will go before you,

and the God of Israel

will be your rear guard.

Isaiah 52:12

Reflection Question:

This passage begins with a celebration telling Zion to wake up, put on strength and put on their beautiful garments. The time of judgement is over. God has shown his holy arm before all the nations. The other nations who oppressed them have been brought low and it is time for rejoicing and singing. They are called to depart and separate from Babylon for the sake of purity and God goes with them—both before and behind them.

Just as God called his people to depart and live separate from the Babylonians, God has called us to separate from the world. Though we are to love the lost and reach out to them with the gospel, for purity sake, we are not to do as they do. We need to live in the world but not be of the world. We must always remember that God is with us. His presence goes before and behind us. We are not alone even when we are standing alone for truth. Is there a relationship in your life that the enemy has used to pull you away from the Lord? Maybe it's not a person but rather someone you follow on social media, music you listen to or a book you are reading. It's time to depart and separate yourself from that thing that is tempting you. Write a prayer below asking the Lord to give you the strength to follow him in this area.

S—The S stands for *Scripture*

O—The O stands for *Observation*

A—The A stands for *Application*

K—The K stands for *Kneeling in Prayer*

But he was wounded for our transgressions;

he was crushed for our iniquities;

upon him was the chastisement that brought us peace,

and by his wounds we are healed.

Isaiah 53:5

Reflection Question:

Isaiah prophesied of the coming Messiah. He anticipated a Messiah that would suffer and be rejected. He would not have a physical beauty that would cause people to desire him. Like a lamb to the slaughter, he would be oppressed and afflicted, yet not open his mouth. He would bear our grief and sorrows and be crushed for our iniquities. By his wounds we would be healed.

Oh, what a wonderful Savior Jesus is! Isaiah said that the coming Messiah would not have a form of physical beauty that would make people desire him. Our culture puts far more value on physical beauty than God does. Jesus did not use the benefit of good looks to attract people to him. Sometimes in the church we are tempted to present the gospel in fancy ways to draw unbelievers. While it's good to carefully present the gospel in the clearest way possible, it is not necessary to go over the top. How does knowing that Jesus did not use his outer appearance to attract people to him, free you from the pressure to speak eloquently when giving the gospel? How does knowing that God does not value physical beauty the same way man does, free you from the pressure to pursue physical beauty the way the world does?

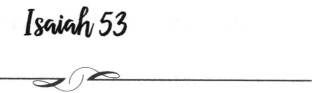

S—The S stands for *Scripture*

O—The O stands for *Observation*

A—The A stands for *Application*

K—The K stands for *Kneeling in Prayer*

For your Maker is your husband,

the Lord of hosts is his name;

and the Holy One of Israel is your Redeemer,

the God of the whole earth he is called.

Isaiah 54:5

Reflection Question:

As the Lord restores Israel, he comforts them and promises to never forsake them. He is their maker, their husband, the Lord of hosts, the Holy One, their redeemer and the God of the whole earth. Like a woman who is barren or a wife who has been deserted, he removes their shame. He promises his people peace and protection.

Israel was not only taken captive by their enemies, but they were disgraced and humiliated. God not only released them from captivity, but he also removed their disgrace and humiliation, and he gave them the greatest gift of all --- himself. Is there an area of your life where you have been embarrassed or humiliated? Satan is the father of lies and he wants you to live in the shadow of shame rather than freedom. The God of the whole earth, who is your maker, loves you deeply and has removed all of your past sin and shame. In what area of your life has the enemy taken you captive? Do not let the enemy destroy you any further. Today is the day you must give this to God and start living in freedom.

Isaiah 54

S—The S stands for *Scripture*

O—The O stands for *Observation*

A—The A stands for *Application*

K—The K stands for *Kneeling in Prayer*

So shall my word be that goes out from my mouth;

it shall not return to me empty,

but it shall accomplish that which I purpose,

and shall succeed in the thing for which I sent it.

Isaiah 55:11

Reflection Question:

God's thoughts and ways are so much higher than ours. God does not think the way we think or act the way we act. The difference between our ways and his ways is the distance between the heavens and the earth. That's a big difference! When he speaks, it accomplishes what it is supposed to accomplish. His word is powerful and does not return empty. It never fails to accomplish his intended purpose.

Sometimes it is hard to understand God. I'm embarrassed to admit that there are times I have prayed and been frustrated that God did not take my advice as to how he could solve a problem of mine. But his perspective, his plans, his purposes and his will are so much greater than ours. This should not discourage us but rather comfort us. We can trust him. What has studying God's word accomplished in your life? How does considering the great wisdom and power of God and his thoughts, ways and word - help you trust him more?

S—The S stands for *Scripture*

O—The O stands for *Observation*

A—The A stands for *Application*

K—The K stands for *Kneeling in Prayer*

For my house shall be called

a house of prayer

for all peoples.

Isaiah 56:7

Reflection Question:

God wanted his house to not just be a house of prayer for his people but also for foreigners as well. Israel had not considered that God's love would spread to those outside their borders. Their years of captivity and pain at the hands of foreigners led them to believe that only they were accepted, and all others would be rejected. But Isaiah tells them that the foreigners burnt offerings and sacrifices would be accepted too.

I am so thankful that the Lord accepts the outcasts and foreigners because that means he accepts me! In Matthew 21:13 we see the anger of Jesus displayed when the outer courts of the temple, which is the only place where the Gentiles could pray, had been turned into a marketplace. Jesus quotes Isaiah 56:7 when he says: *"It is written, My house shall be called a house of prayer, but you make it a den of robbers."*

Jesus made a way for both you and me to be acceptable in the sight of the Lord. God's design and purpose for his house is that it would be a place of worship and prayer for all. Are you a member of a local church? Do you attend regularly and pray there? If not, I encourage you to find a local church this week. If you are a regular, who is someone who may be a bit of an outcast or a foreigner that you could invite to church.

Isaiah 56

S—The S stands for *Scripture*

O—The O stands for *Observation*

A—The A stands for *Application*

K—The K stands for *Kneeling in Prayer*

"There is no peace,"

says my God, "for the wicked."

Isaiah 57:21

Reflection Question:

God, in his great love and mercy, heals and restores. He gives peace to those both far and near, to the Gentiles and the Jews. But the wicked are like a tossing sea that cannot be quieted. The moving waters toss up mire and dirt. There is no peace for the wicked.

When we examine the lives of those who are not honoring God, it can appear as though they have a life of peace and rest. But Jesus told us in John 14:27, that he gives us a peace that the world cannot give. This world can offer peace on a good day but it's an illusion because the very next day something can change, and that peace can be lost. Those who seek peace from the world will find that they have to continually exhaust themselves pursuing it or participate in wickedness to get that peace and maintain it. The pursuit of "happiness" from the world can lead to wickedness. In what ways have you sought to find peace and rest from the world? How has this type of peace fallen short? How is the peace that God has given you different than the world's peace?

S—The S stands for *Scripture*

O—The O stands for *Observation*

A—The A stands for *Application*

K—The K stands for *Kneeling in Prayer*

If you pour yourself out for the hungry

and satisfy the desire of the afflicted,

then shall your light rise in the darkness

and your gloom be as the noonday.

Isaiah 58:10

Reflection Question:

Isaiah compares two types of fasting. One is hollow, empty and for show. The people did the right things with the wrong heart. They appeared spiritual but under the surface they were full of selfishness. The Lord did not answer their prayers. Then he compares this type of fasting with those who are sincere and seek to honor God. Pleasing God began with how they treated others. He says when they feed the hungry, give to the poor, care for those in their family and help the oppressed, God would hear and answer their prayers. Blessings would be poured out on them, as their gloom would be turned to joy. God would be their guide and strengthen them.

Pleasing God begins with how we treat others. Have you ever considered that how you love others can affect your prayer life? Isaiah shows us that when we pour our lives out for others, the darkness in our own lives begins to lift. How have you experienced joy in the past, when you have cared for the needs of the hungry, poor or oppressed? Have you struggled with unanswered prayers and felt down and discouraged lately? Consider, taking your eyes off of your own problems today and reaching out to someone in need who has it worse off. Be the answer to their prayers.

S—The S stands for *Scripture*

O—The O stands for *Observation*

A—The A stands for *Application*

K—The K stands for *Kneeling in Prayer*

The Lord's hand is not shortened,

that it cannot save,

or his ear dull, that it cannot hear.

Isaiah 59:1

Reflection Question:

Isaiah starts out chapter 59 with the word "behold". Behold means to pause and focus your thoughts. Observe this truth. The Lord's hand is not too short to save or ear too dull to hear. We have an all-powerful sovereign God, and he can hear just fine. The problem was their sin. Their sin had separated them from God. As a result, God's face felt hidden from them and it felt like he was not hearing them.

Do you ever feel like God is hidden? Or like you are praying but God is not hearing you? God is with you. He will never leave you nor forsake you (Hebrews 13:5). Because of Jesus' death on the cross and his payment for our sins, we are forgiven and no longer separated from God. But sin in our lives can break our fellowship with God. It lures us away from his heart and as a result we may reap what we have sown. We may miss out on blessings or reap painful consequences and it can feel like God is far away. Is there sin in your life you need to confess? Have you been tempted to blame God for a difficult circumstance in your life that your own sin has caused? God is near and he hears your every prayer. Confess your sin today. Jesus loves you.

S—The S stands for *Scripture*

O—The O stands for *Observation*

A—The A stands for *Application*

K—The K stands for *Kneeling in Prayer*

Arise, shine,

for your light has come,

and the glory of the Lord

has risen upon you.

Isaiah 60:1

Reflection Question:

For the last two chapters we have seen God's people wrestle with darkness. But now, in chapter 60, the light has come and so God tells his people to rise and shine! In verse 19, he says that one day, the sun shall be no more for the Lord will be our everlasting light. The sun will no longer need to go down and they'll be no need for the moon. We will live in light forever. This prophecy is also given in Revelation 21:22-23, where John speaks of the New Jerusalem and he says: *"And I saw no temple in the city, for its temple is the Lord God the Almighty and the Lamb. And the city has no need of sun or moon to shine on it, for the glory of God gives it light, and its lamp is the Lamb."*

We are so used to our lives being divided into night and day. But one day in heaven, there will be no more night. It will always be daytime. We will have no need for a place of worship because God's presence will always be with us. What a great hope this is! The light of the world has come and so now, we must walk in the light. Are you shining so others can see that you are walking in the light? In what ways is your walk with God evident in your lifestyle?

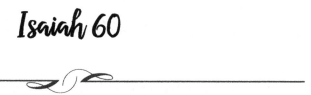

S—The S stands for *Scripture*

O—The O stands for *Observation*

A—The A stands for *Application*

K—The K stands for *Kneeling in Prayer*

The Lord has anointed me

to bring good news to the poor;

he has sent me to bind up the brokenhearted,

to proclaim liberty to the captives,

and the opening of the prison to those who are bound.

Isaiah 61:1

Reflection Question:

Isaiah begins this chapter prophesying about the coming Messiah. In Luke 4:16-22, Jesus stood up in the synagogue, opened the scroll to Isaiah 61 and read this exact passage. Then he said, *"today this scripture has been fulfilled in your hearing."*

Jesus was sent to bring good news to the poor, to heal the brokenhearted, and to free those oppressed by sin. It says in verse 3, that he gives those who are mourning - a beautiful headdress instead of ashes. Life can be very difficult sometimes. We live in a harsh world where unfair things happen, hearts are broken and loved ones are lost. But in the midst of our pain and sorrow, God is there with us. He wants to bring beauty from our ashes and set us free. Do you feel stuck today in sin or pain or sorrow? What is causing you to feel this way? Write a prayer below giving your pain to Jesus—ask him to restore you and exchange beauty for your ashes.

S—The S stands for *Scripture*

O—The O stands for *Observation*

A—The A stands for *Application*

K—The K stands for *Kneeling in Prayer*

You shall be a crown of beauty
in the hand of the Lord,
and a royal diadem
in the hand of your God.

Isaiah 62:3

Reflection Question:

God loves his people so very much. They are a precious crown of beauty to him. Zion's coming salvation would reveal that they were not a forsaken people and like a bridegroom rejoices over his bride, so God rejoices over his people.

God doesn't just love his children; he rejoices over them. This is also written in Zephaniah 3:17, where it says: *"The Lord your God is in your midst, a mighty one who will save; he will rejoice over you with gladness; he will quiet you by his love; he will exult over you with loud singing."*

Just as we sing and rejoice in the Lord, God sings. Can you imagine God singing? And can you imagine God singing because he is rejoicing over you? I don't think we can fully comprehend the depth of God's love for us and we underestimate the joy he takes in us. But Zephaniah says his love quiets us. How does knowing God sings and rejoices over you, quiet you.

S—The S stands for *Scripture*

O—The O stands for *Observation*

A—The A stands for *Application*

K—The K stands for *Kneeling in Prayer*

I will recount

the steadfast love of the Lord.

Isaiah 63:7

Reflection Question:

God is not only mighty to save; he is mighty to judge. He alone is the only one who can judge, and he judges to avenge his redeemed. Isaiah recounts the Lord's great mercy and steadfast love, even while they are in exile. He is a loving father who felt their pain with them but even in his great mercy, they rebelled against him. Their hearts were hard, and they turned against him.

God's love is steadfast. That means his love for us is faithful, loyal and sure. He is a covenant keeping God who keeps his word to us. Even when we are at our lowest, his love for us is unwavering. Take a moment to recount God's steadfast love for you. Write below about a time when you turned your back on God or disobeyed him and you experienced his mercy and steadfast love. Then praise him for his love toward you in both the good and bad times.

Isaiah 63

S—The S stands for *Scripture*

O—The O stands for *Observation*

A—The A stands for *Application*

K—The K stands for *Kneeling in Prayer*

From of old no one has heard
or perceived by the ear,
no eye has seen a God besides you,
who acts for those who wait for him.

Isaiah 64:4

Reflection Question:

Isaiah begs God to come down from heaven and make his presence known. He wants him to intervene with his great power. From the beginning of the world, no eye has seen, or ear has heard of a God like Israel's God. He knows that God blesses those who wait for him, but he also knows that God only answers the prayer of the righteous and Israel had sinned.

Waiting on God to work in our lives is hard. It is tempting to try to intervene with our own ideas and plans and get ahead of God. We know that he is all powerful and can help us but when he doesn't, it can be hard to wait for God. Think of a time when you waited on God and you saw him work things out for you. Now consider, what area of your life are you currently waiting on God? Take strength in knowing that God has done it before, and he will do it again. Trust him as you wait.

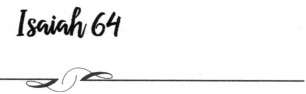

S—The S stands for *Scripture*

O—The O stands for *Observation*

A—The A stands for *Application*

K—The K stands for *Kneeling in Prayer*

Before they call, I will answer;

while they are yet speaking, I will hear.

Isaiah 65:24

Reflection Question:

We see at the start of chapter 65 those who were not seeking God, find God. Isaiah was speaking of the Gentiles. Paul quotes Isaiah 65:1 in Romans 10:20, as he speaks of Gentiles being grafted into the family of God. God's plan of salvation for all the nations is beautiful and one day he will make a new heaven, a new earth and a new Jerusalem. Then, Isaiah describes the millennial kingdom as he moves from one time frame to another. During this time, there will be such closeness with God that he will answer his people before they even call out to him.

Isaiah gives us such a wonderful promise of a glorious future with the Lord. Our God is omniscient and all knowing. He knows our every thought and word before we speak it. He hears all of our prayers. He responds to our cries when we callout to him. And though he may not always answer the way we hope he would, we can trust that he is working all things out for our good and his glory. How does it make you feel to know that he knows your every thought and word before you speak it? Does that make you cringe, or does that comfort you? Consider how close God's presence is to you right now and rest in his love and care for you today.

S—The S stands for *Scripture*

O—The O stands for *Observation*

A—The A stands for *Application*

K—The K stands for *Kneeling in Prayer*

As one whom his mother comforts,

so I will comfort you.

Isaiah 66:13

Reflection Question:

As the book of Isaiah closes, we see the Lord on his throne in heaven, sovereign over all the earth. He gives peace to his people like a flowing river and he speaks gently and tenderly to his children, like a mother would. In the end, God triumphs as the nations are judged and his people are redeemed. The book has a sober ending as Isaiah gives a contrast between those who worship God and those who rebelled and will suffer eternal judgement.

God chose the picture of a mother to explain his comfort and care for his people. While a father can be a comforter, there is something special about the comfort of a nursing mother to her child. In John 14:26, Jesus says he has given us the Holy Spirit as a comforter. He is with us and never leaves us. Is there an area in your life where you are in need of comfort? God is with you. Give him your pain and sorrow. Lean hard on him today. He loves you so much.

Keep walking with the King.

S—The S stands for *Scripture*

O—The O stands for *Observation*

A—The A stands for *Application*

K—The K stands for *Kneeling in Prayer*

Made in the USA
Monee, IL
02 January 2022